Farmer
and the
Brown Pony

written by Jay Dale

illustrated by Lisa Fox

"Can I have a ride
on the little grey pony?"
said Jim.

"No," said Farmer Pat.
"The grey pony
is too little for you."

"Look!" said Jim.

"I can see a brown pony.

Can I ride that pony?"

"Yes," said Farmer Pat.

"You can ride

the brown pony."

Farmer Pat helped Jim
to get on the brown pony.

"Look at me!" shouted Jim.
"I am sitting
on the brown pony."

"Come on, brown pony,"
said Jim.
"We can go down the path."

The brown pony did not go.

"Come on!" said Jim.

"I can ride you today."

The brown pony did not go.

"Come on, brown pony,"
said Farmer Pat.
"You can go up and down
the path with me."

"Look at me!" shouted Jim.

"I can ride the brown pony."